FIRST GUITAR RIFFS

Wise Publications
London/New York/Paris/Sydney/Copenhagen/Madrid

Exclusive Distributors:
Music Sales Limited
8/9 Frith Street,
London W1V 5TZ, England.
Music Sales Pty Limited
120 Rothschild Avenue,
Rosebery, NSW 2018,
Australia.

Order No.AM91073
ISBN 0.7119.3404.5
This book © Copyright 1993 by Wise Publications

Cover design by Pearce Marchbank, Studio Twenty
Cover photography by George Taylor
Compiled and arranged by Arthur Dick
Computer management by Adam Hay Editorial Design
Music processed by The Pitts

Printed in the United Kingdom by
J.B. Offset Printers (Marks Tey) Limited, Marks Tey, Essex.

Your Guarantee of Quality
As publishers, we strive to produce every book to
the highest commercial standards.
Particular care has been given to specifying acid-free,
neutral-sized paper which has not been chlorine bleached but
produced with special regard for the environment. Throughout,
the printing and binding have been planned to ensure a sturdy,
attractive publication which should give years of enjoyment.
If your copy fails to meet our high standards,
please inform us and we will gladly replace it.

Music Sales' complete catalogue lists thousands of titles
and is free from your local music shop,
or direct from Music Sales Limited.
Please send a cheque/postal order for £1.50 for postage to:
Music Sales Limited, Newmarket Road,
Bury St. Edmunds, Suffolk IP33 3YB.

In this book we will use both standard musical notation, used by all musicians, and guitar tablature, a simplified diagram-style system peculiar to the guitar.

Standard music notation uses a set of 5 lines, called the stave or staff. Note symbols are placed on lines and the spaces between the lines to denote the various musical sounds.

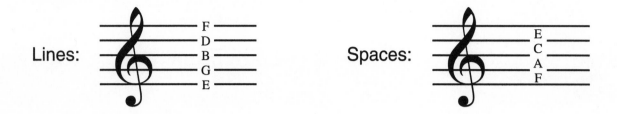

Lines:

Spaces:

We can also extend the range of the notation above and below the stave's 5 lines:

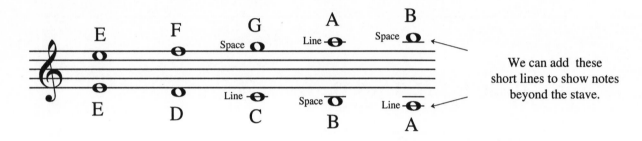

We can add these short lines to show notes beyond the stave.

F♯   B♭

If the symbol ♯ is placed in front of a note in a piece of music, the note found next to the sign is sharpened (raised one fret).

If the symbol ♭ is placed in front of a note in a piece of music, the note found next to the sign is flattened (lowered by one fret).

The symbol ♮ cancels the previous ♯ or ♭.

F♯   F♯

If a sharp ♯ or flat ♭ sign is placed at the beginning of a stave in front of the time signature, it means that all the notes in the piece that occur on this line or anywhere on the stave are affected.

Music is comprised of sounds of different lengths. We have a simple system for describing the duration of musical notes:

Whole Note	Half Note	Quarter Note	Eighth Note	Sixteenth Note
4 beats long	2 beats long	1 beat long	½ beat long	¼ beat long

The two numbers at the start of this example are the 'time signature'.
Here this means the music is divided into units equal to 4 quarter notes (units of four beats each).

In this example the music is grouped into units of 3 beats each.

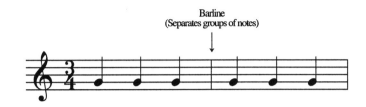

These are Repeat Signs:

The music between these signs is to be repeated. If the symbol on the left hand side does not appear, then go back to the beginning.

Where the ending of the 'second time through' is different from the first, then 1st and 2nd time bars are used:

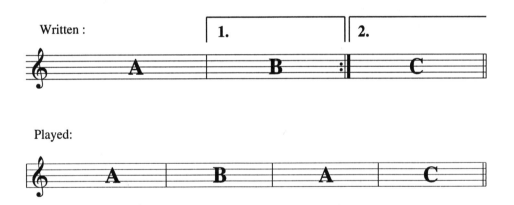

D.S. (dal segno) means return to the Sign 𝄋

Al Coda means play as far as the Coda symbol ⊕ (To Coda) then go straight to the end section marked again with the Coda symbol ⊕

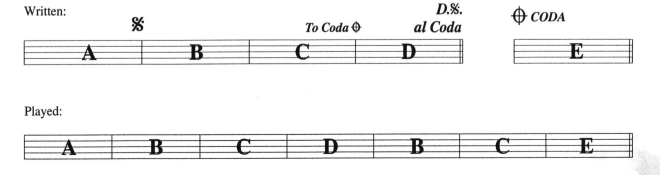

Tablature and Instructions explained

In these next two pages you will find some symbols not used in this book. However you will need to be familiar with them when you progress to other Guitar TAB books from the Music Sales Catalogue.

The tablature stave comprises six lines, each representing a string on the guitar as illustrated.

A number on any of the lines indicates, therefore, the string and fret on which a note should be played.

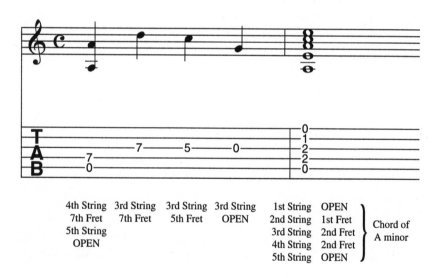

4th String	3rd String	3rd String	3rd String	1st String	OPEN	
7th Fret	7th Fret	5th Fret	OPEN	2nd String	1st Fret	
5th String				3rd String	2nd Fret	Chord of
OPEN				4th String	2nd Fret	A minor
				5th String	OPEN	

A useful hint to help you read tablature is to cut out small squares of self-adhesive paper and stick them on the upper edge of the guitar neck adjacent to each of the frets, numbering them accordingly. Be careful to use paper that will not damage the finish on your guitar.

Finger Vibrato

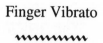

Tremolo Arm Vibrato

Glissando

Strike the note, then slide the finger up or down the fretboard as indicated.

Tremolo Strumming

This sign indicates fast up and down stroke strumming.

8va

This sign indicates that the notes are to be played an octave higher than written.

loco

This instruction cancels the above.

This note-head indicates the string is to be totally muted to produce a percussive effect.

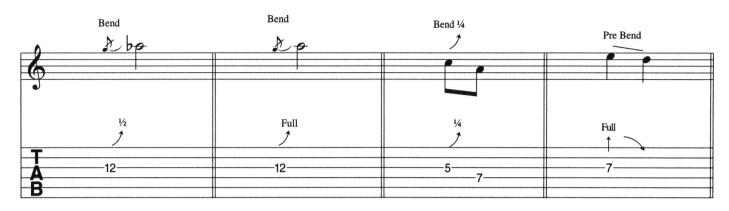

HALF TONE BEND

Play the note G then bend the string so that the pitch rises by a half tone (semi-tone).

FULL TONE BEND

DECORATIVE BEND

PRE BEND

Bend the string as indicated, strike the string and release.

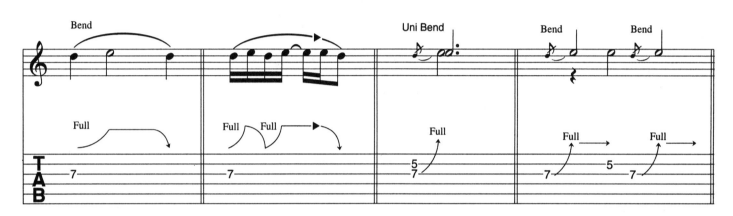

BEND & RELEASE

Strike the string, bend it as indicated, then release the bend whilst it is still sounding.

BEND & RESTRIKE

Strike the string, bend or gliss as indicated, then restrike the string where the symbol occurs.

UNISON BEND

Strike both strings simultaneously then immediately bend the lower string as indicated.

STAGGERED UNISON BEND

Strike the lower string and bend as indicated, whilst it is still sounding strike the higher string.

HAMMER ON

Hammer a finger down on the next note without striking the string again.

PULL OFF

Pull your finger off the string with a plucking motion to sound the next note without striking the string again.

RAKE UP

Strum the notes upwards in the manner of an arpeggio.

RAKE DOWN

Strum the notes downwards in the manner of an arpeggio.

HARMONICS

Strike the string whilst touching it lightly at the fret position shown. Artificial Harmonics will be described in context.

Accurate tuning of the guitar is essential.

The guitar can be tuned with the aid of pitch pipes or dedicated electronic guitar tuners which are available through your local music dealer.

If you do not have a tuning device, you can use relative tuning.

Relative Tuning

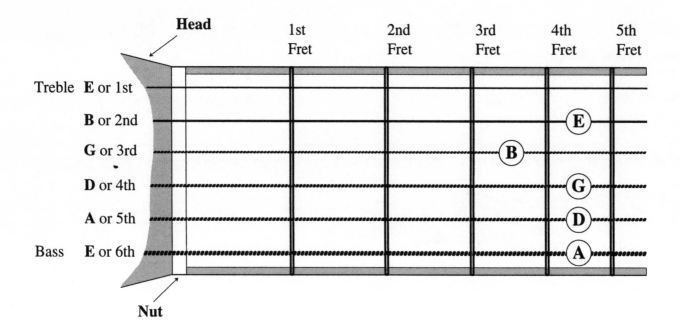

Press down where indicated, one at a time, following the instructions below.

Estimate the pitch of the 6th string as near as possible to E or at least a comfortable pitch (not too high, as you might break other strings in tuning up).

Then, while checking the various positions on the above diagram, place a finger from your left hand on:

the 5th fret of the E or 6th string and **tune the open A** (or 5th string) to the note (A)

the 5th fret of the A or 5th string and **tune the open D** (or 4th string) to the note (D)

the 5th fret of the D or 4th string and **tune the open G** (or 3rd string) to the note (G)

the 4th fret of the G or 3rd string and **tune the open B** (or 2nd string) to the note (B)

the 5th fret of the B or 2nd string and **tune the open E** (or 1st string) to the note (E)

The guitar has a unique place in the history of Rock, Pop and Jazz music. Whatever the style you want to play, you will find this collection of essential riffs invaluable.

In the hands of an expert the guitar can take on an almost human quality in its phrasing and articulation, making it a brilliantly expressive instrument.

To show you how this is done, many of the riffs in this book include embellishments such as string bending, hammering-on, pulling-off and glissandi (sliding from one fret to another). The music on the staves and TAB systems includes specific instructions for all of these.

Let's take a simple riff and develop it using some basic techniques. Play the riff in Example 1 without any embellishments to begin with. Strike each note with even down-strokes.

Example 1

Now let's play the same riff, but this time pull off the D to the open B, i.e. play the first note then pull off from the third fret to sound the open B without re-striking the string (Example 2).

Example 2

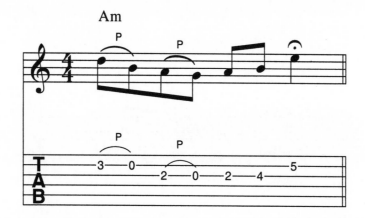

In Example 3 the first part of the riff uses these pull-offs, but the following notes are played by a 'hammering-on' action. To play the hammer-on fret and play the A with your first finger, then play the next note by hammering your third finger on the fourth fret without re-striking the string with your right hand (Example 3).

Example 3

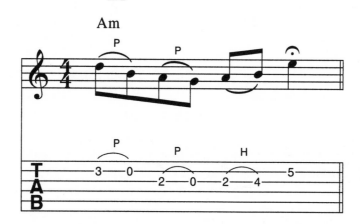

Now let's try the same idea but, rather than hammering on to the fourth fret, slide your finger from one fret to the other, i.e. fret and play the A on the second fret, then slide your finger up to the B on the fourth fret without re-striking the string (Example 4).

Example 4

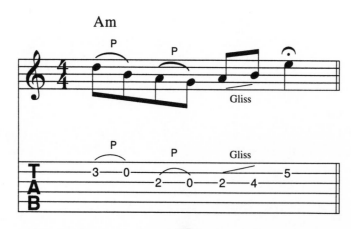

Other possibilities can be created depending on how you want the phrase to sound. For example both Bs can be played on the open second string, and a hammer-on and glissando can be added, as the following example shows (Example 5).

Example 5

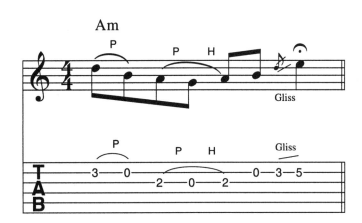

The glissando to the E begins on the D at the third fret on the second string. The grace note ($\flat$) indicates that the D should be played on the beat and raised to the E as quickly as possible.

A full list of TAB instructions is set out in the TAB key at the beginning of this book. For a more detailed explanation of TAB and how it works, refer to our 'Sounding Out TAB' book and cassette pack (order number AM91099), available through your music dealer or direct from Music Sales.

All the examples we have seen so far can be played against a chord of A minor. You will notice that throughout the book each riff has a chord symbol, or series of symbols (a progression) written above it. In each case play the chord first, then the riff to see how they sound in relation to one another. Better still, get a friend to play the chords while you practise the riffs!

Many riffs are made up of notes from a particular scale (e.g. the scale of A minor for Examples 1 -5). By learning these scales and re-arranging them into your own patterns you can create your own riffs. For further information on scales and how they work refer to 'First Scales' (order number AM91074). Once you feel comfortable with what you are doing start to experiment. Music should be fun - take some risks!

The riffs in this book will give you an impressive vocabulary of musical ideas; your jamming will immediately sound more fluent and professional. Remember, though, that Rome wasn't built in a day. Start slowly, check the fingering for each riff, and play each phrase carefully until it feels comfortable. It is a good idea to play each riff straight (with no hammer-ons, bends etc.) until you become fluent, then add the special guitar techniques when you feel totally in control of what you are playing.

Let's begin with some open E riffs.

Remember to play them straight until you are comfortable with them.

Riff 1

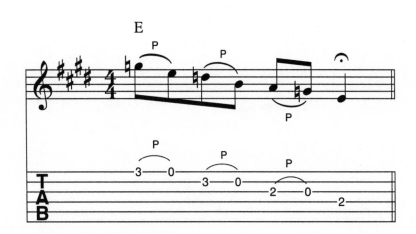

In riff 2 the ascending line can be played by hammering-on as indicated.

Riff 2

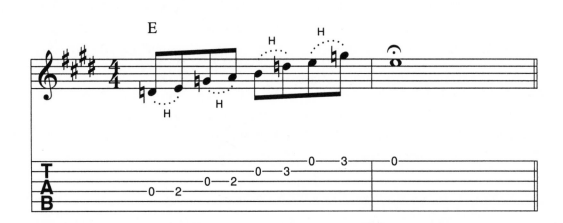

Riff 3

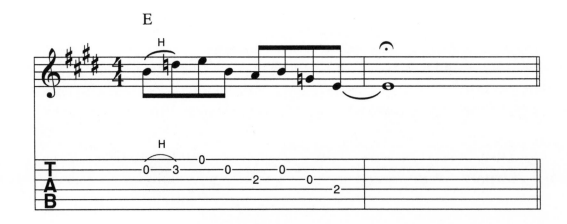

Riff 4

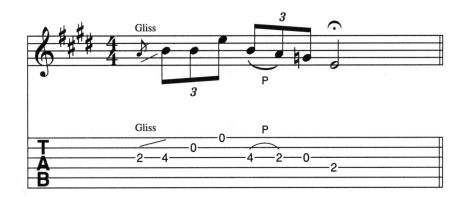

Riff 5

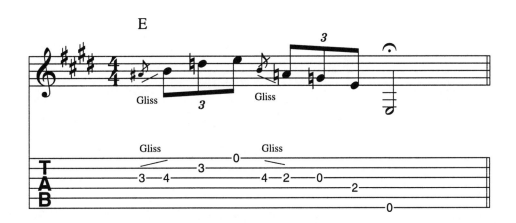

Riff 6

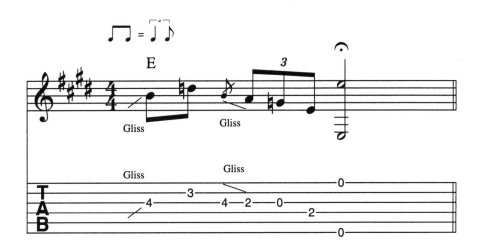

Riff 7

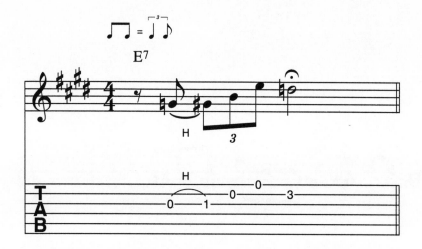

Riff 8

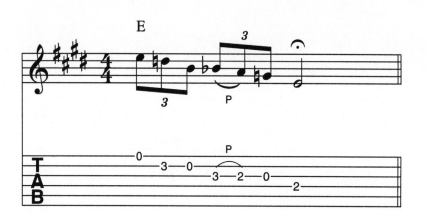

Riff 9

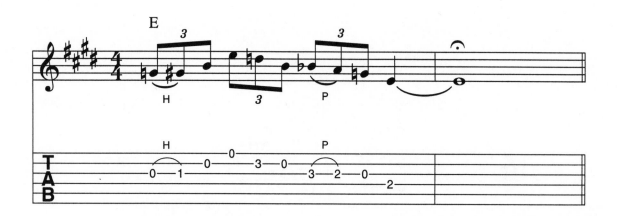

Riff 10

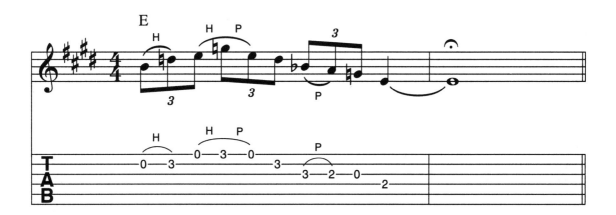

Riff 11

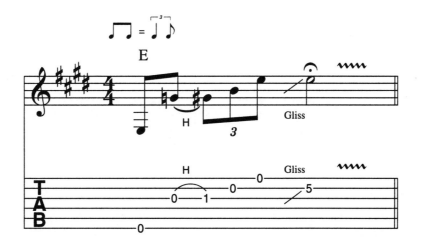

The most famous riff of all must be the twelve bar blues. Play it with a straight feel to begin with, then add swing or shuffle to the rhythm. It can be slow and 'bluesy' or fast and 'rocky'.

Riff 12. The 12 bar blues in E

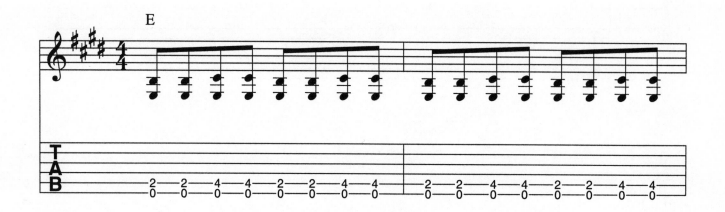

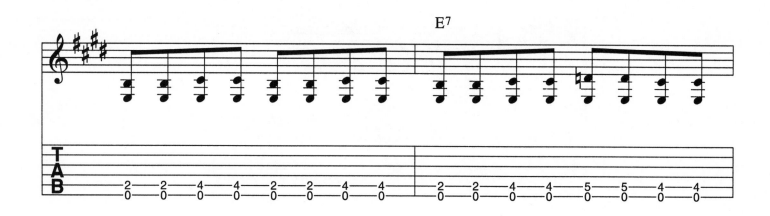

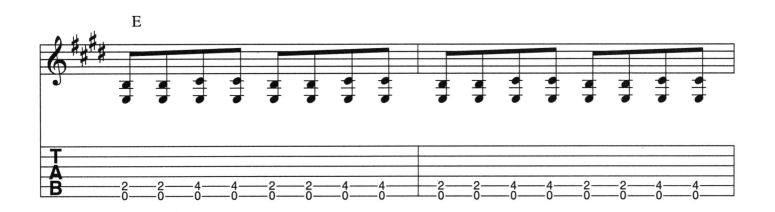

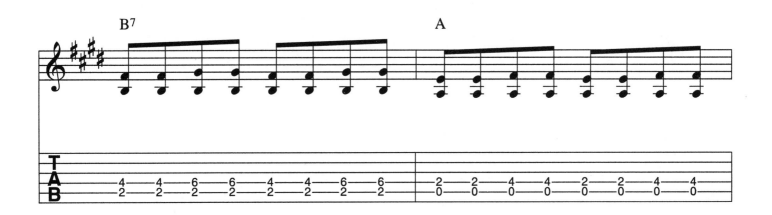

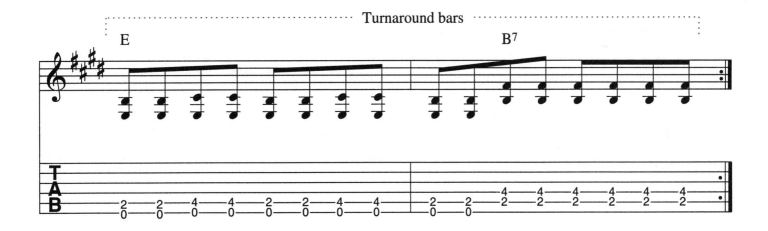

Riffs 1 - 11 can be played with this twelve bar blues. They will work against any of the chords in the progression. However, the turnaround bars (where the chords change more quickly) deserve special attention and they have their own very distinctive riffs. The following riffs are great for the turnaround bars.

Turnaround riffs.

Try substituting these turnaround chords in the last two bars of the blues progression.

Riff 13

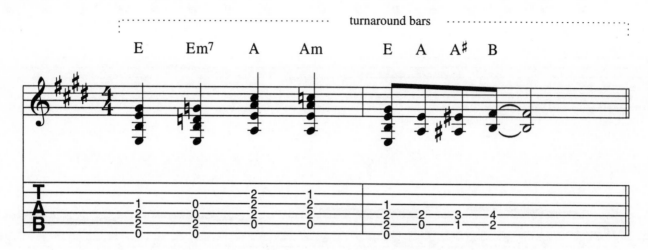

The following solo riffs can be played over the two bar turnaround, with or without the substitute chords.

Riff 14

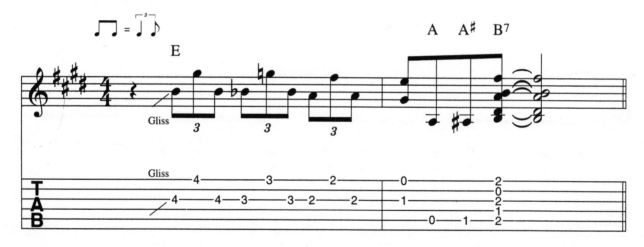

Riff 15

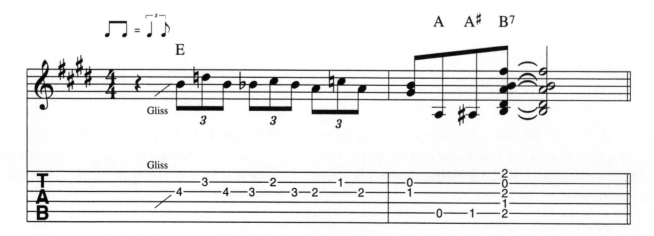

Riff 16

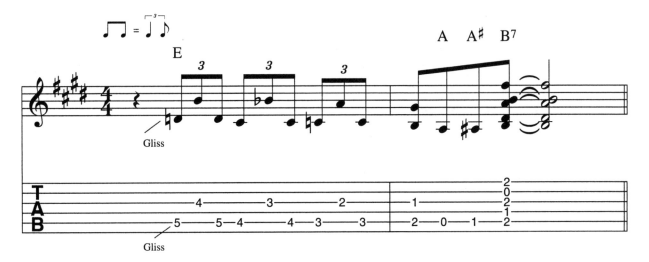

Riff 17

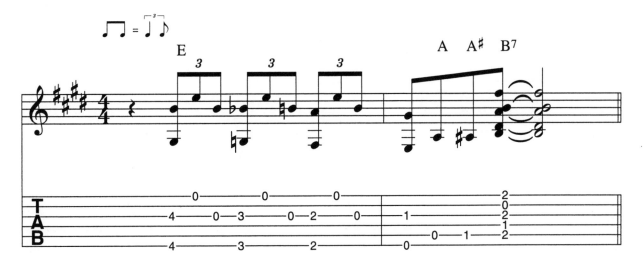

Let's play the blues sequence again, this time in the key of A. Notice that the fingering pattern is similar to the E blues.

Riff 18. The twelve bar blues in A.

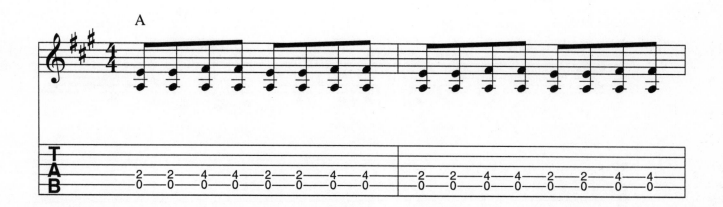

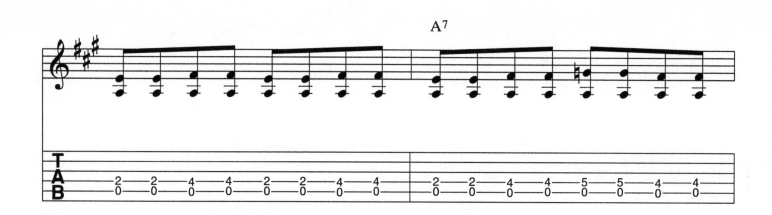

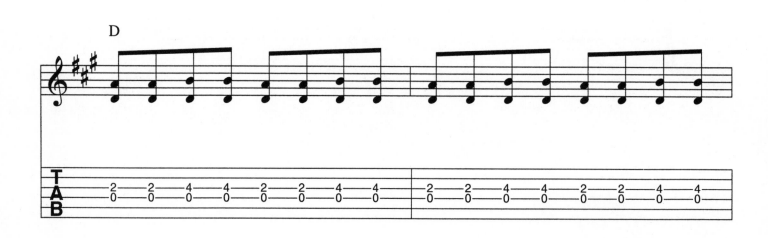

A

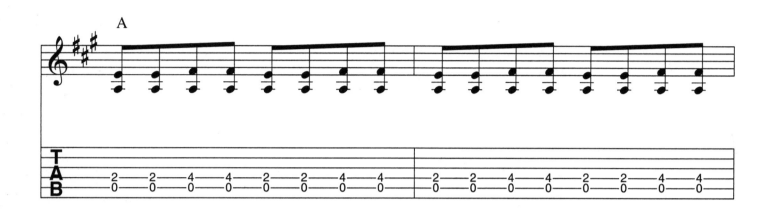

E⁷   D

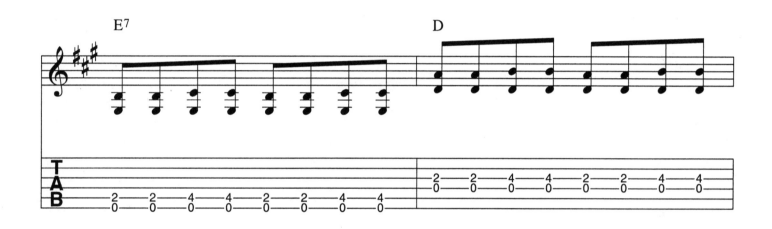

··· Turnaround bars ···

A   E⁷

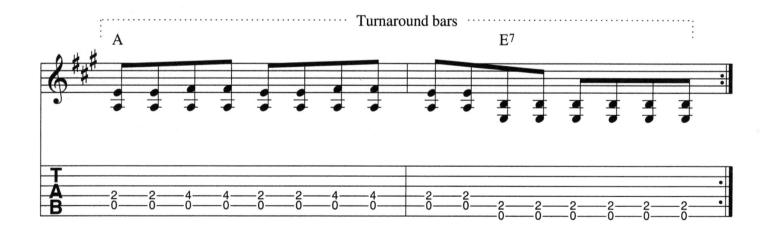

21

Here are some great riffs to play over the twelve bar blues progression. Try experimenting with them or inventing your own ideas to go with them.

Riff 19

Riff 20

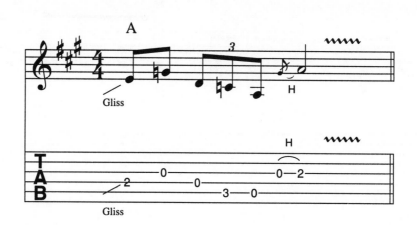

Riff 21

Riff 22

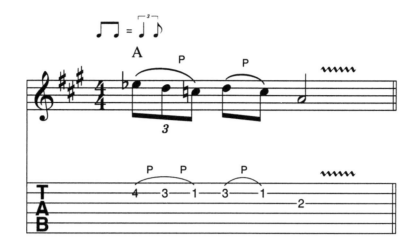

Riff 23

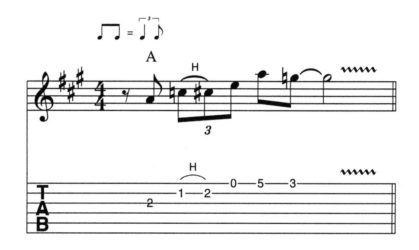

Riff 24

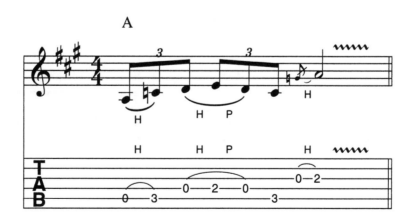

23

Riff 25

Riff 26

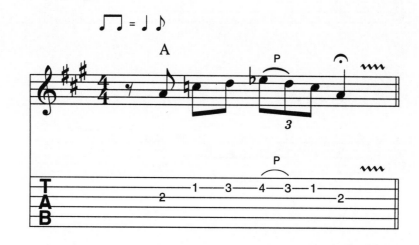

Here are some riffs and substitute chords which can be played over the turnaround bars.

Riff 27

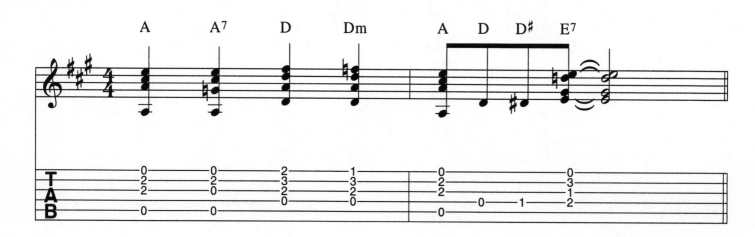

Riff 28

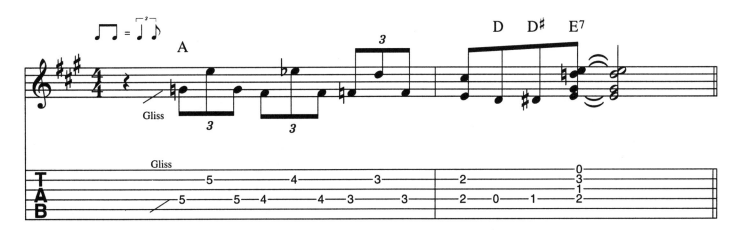

Riff 29

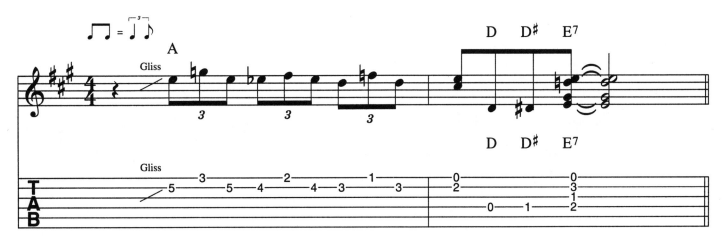

Riff 30

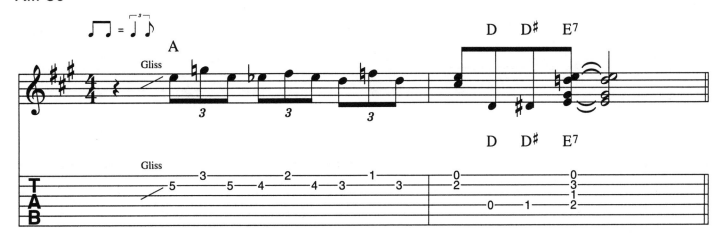

There are many jazz, blues and rock'n'roll phrases which are well suited to the twelve bar blues progression. In each of the following examples pay careful attention to the chord against which the riff is being played.

Riff 31

Riff 32

Riff 33

Riff 34

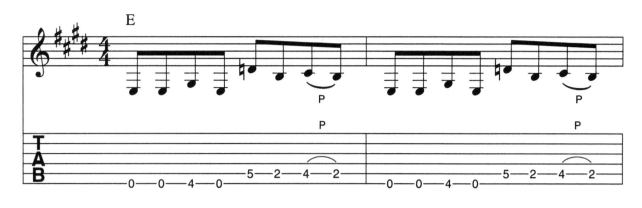

Continuing the idea for the chords of A and B⁷

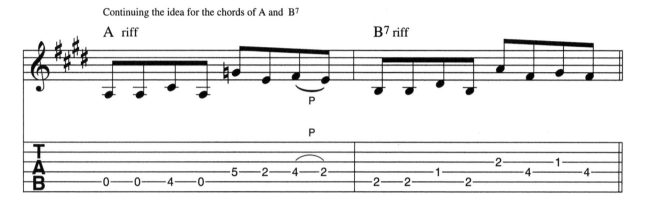

In the following example the E, A and B7 riffs can be played as a twelve bar sequence. As well as introducing the E riff the phrase in bar 1 can 'fill in' between the chord changes. For example, play one bar of the E riff, followed by the opening riff.

Riff 35

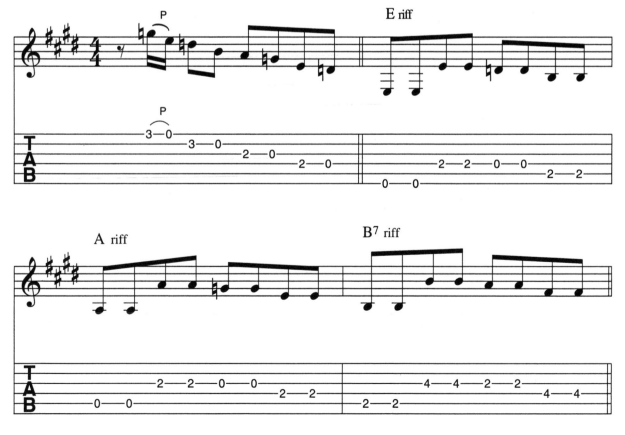

In this example damp the strings with your pick hand, i.e. as you play place your hand over the strings to stop them resonating fully.

Riff 36

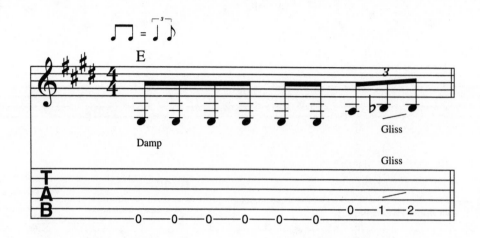

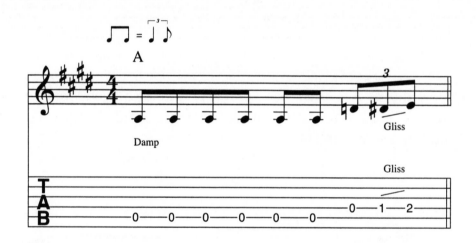

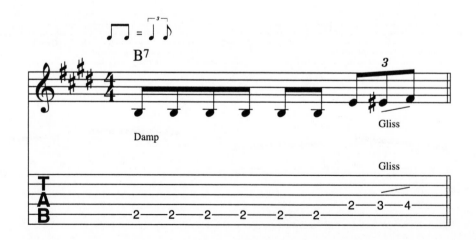

Riff 37

Over a chord of A this riff is best played in the third position.

Riff 38

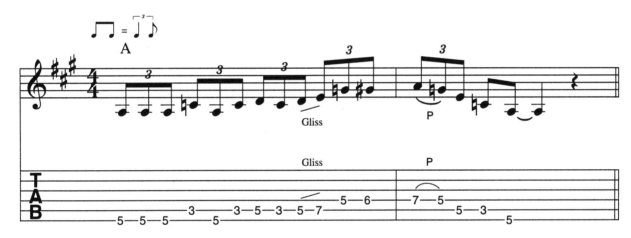

The rhythm of this riff can be freely interpreted. It should be played in the open position.

Riff 39

The following riffs in G are played in the open position, i.e. first finger on the third fret. These position-based riffs can easily be transposed up or down the neck to different keys. For example, if we move two frets up the neck they become riffs in A.

Riff 40

Riff 41

Riffs 42 and 43 can be played over G major or G minor.

Riff 42

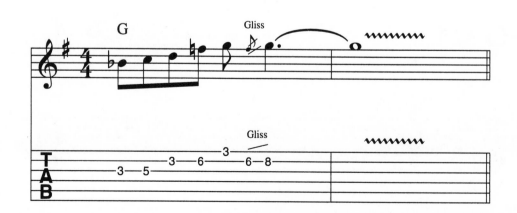

Riff 43

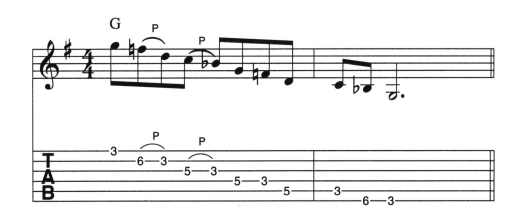

This riff is probably one of the most famous R & B intros ever played. Try transposing it to other keys.

Riff 44

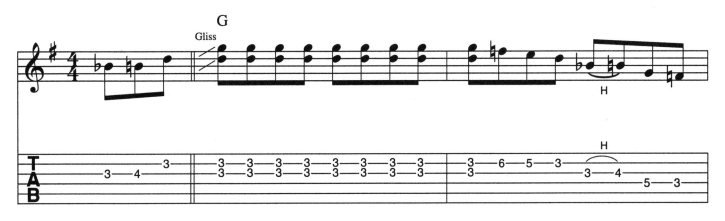

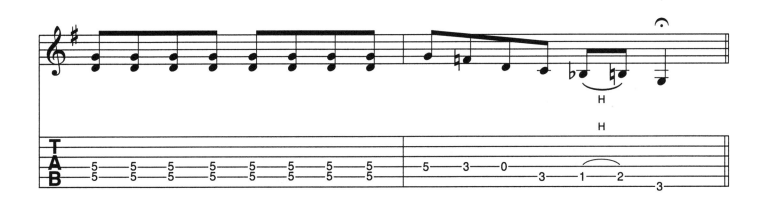

The following are examples of riffs in country, blues and rock styles. Experiment with the phrasing and style.

Riff 45

Riff 46

Riff 47

Riff 48

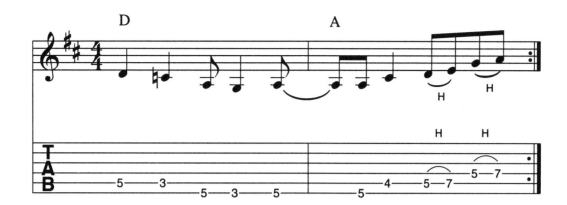

Riff 49

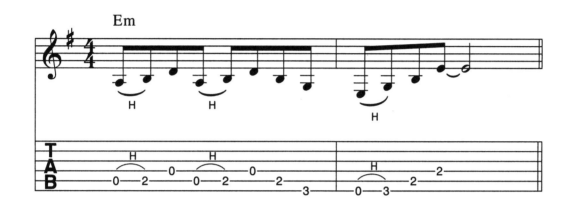

Riff 50

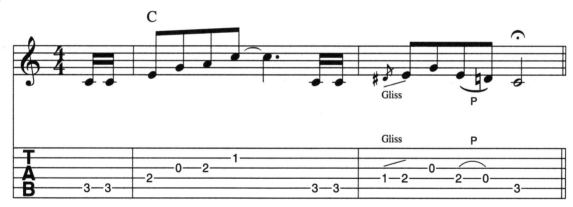

Riff 51

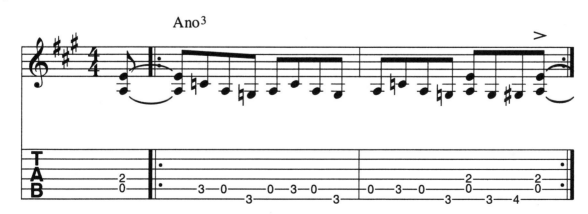

This riff can be played over G minor or as a blues riff over a G7 chord.

Riff 52

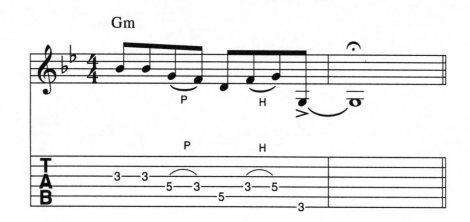

Riff 53

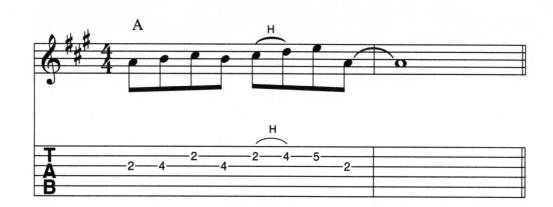

Riff 54

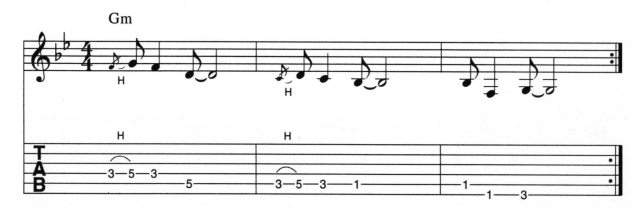

Riff 55

This example of an arpeggio riff should be played allowing the notes to sustain, i.e. let the sound ring.

Riff 56

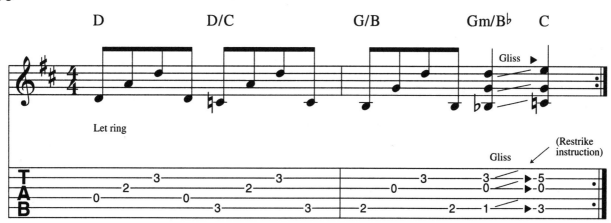

There are many famous riffs whose style you can adopt to make your own. Here are a few variations which are easy to learn. Play each one slowly at first until you are familiar with the finger pattern.

Riff 57 A 60's Rock 'n' Roll riff.

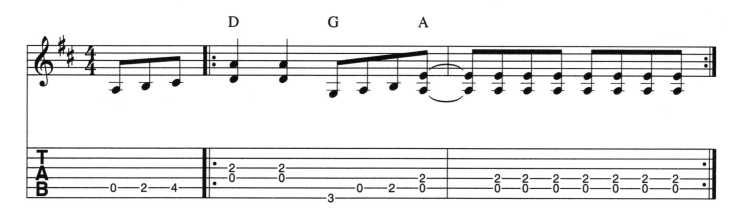

This R.E.M. style riff should be played with a 12 string effect in mind allowing the open strings to sustain.

Riff 58

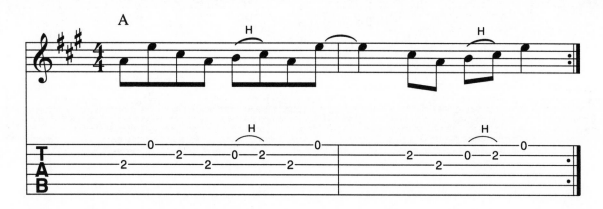

A Beatles style riff. Try and let the notes sustain

Riff 59

These next two examples are 60's style rock/blues riffs and should be played with a rocky feel.

Riff 60

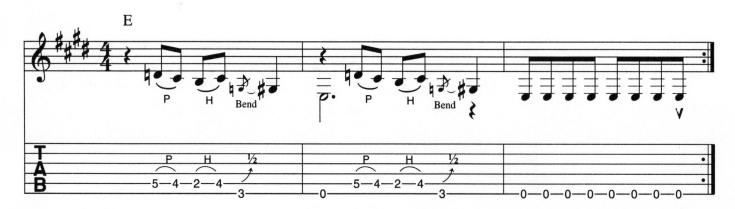

Riff 61

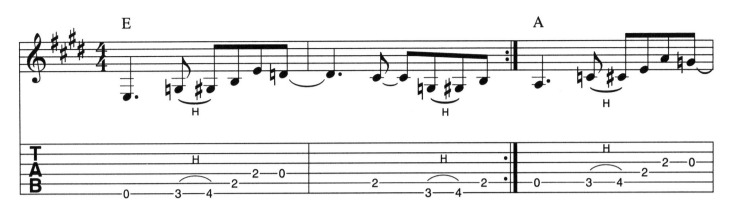

A heavy rock classic played with an overdriven sound for best effect.

Riff 62

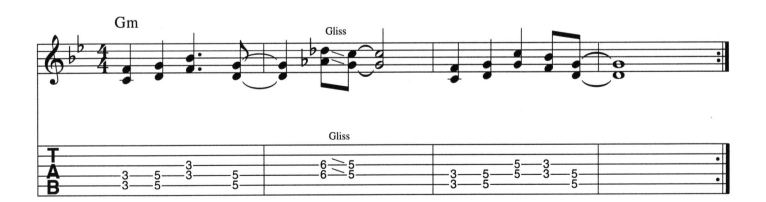

A Bryan Adams style riff played with a clean chorus effect.

Riff 63

This Michael Jackson type riff is best played with a clean funk sound.

Riff 64

The following 3 riffs are arpeggio based. They should be played evenly allowing the notes to ring out.

Riff 65

Riff 66

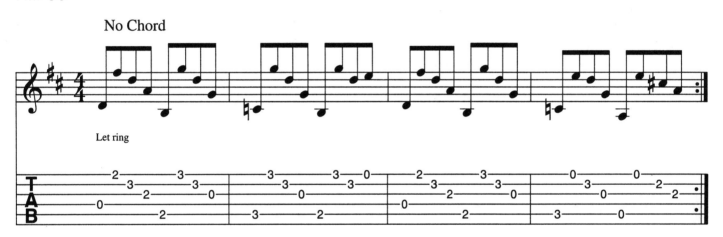

[See over for riff 67]

Riff 67

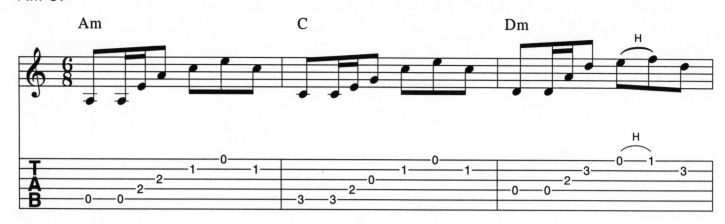

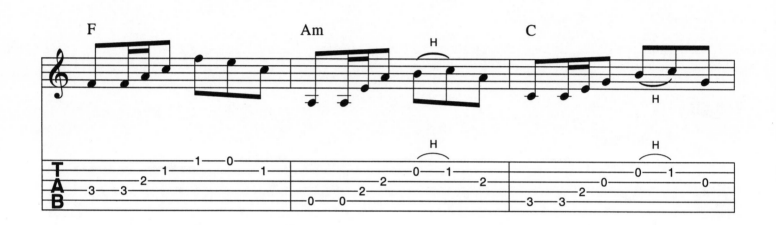

40